Walt Disney's MICKEY MOUSE

GOLDEN®, GOLDEN & DESIGN® and A GOLDEN BOOK®
are trademarks of Western Publishing Company, Inc.

A GOLDEN BOOK®
Western Publishing Company, Inc.
Racine, Wisconsin 53404

WHAT ARE MORTY AND FERDIE EXCITED ABOUT?

Color the spaces with one dot blue, the spaces with two dots red and the spaces with three dots yellow.

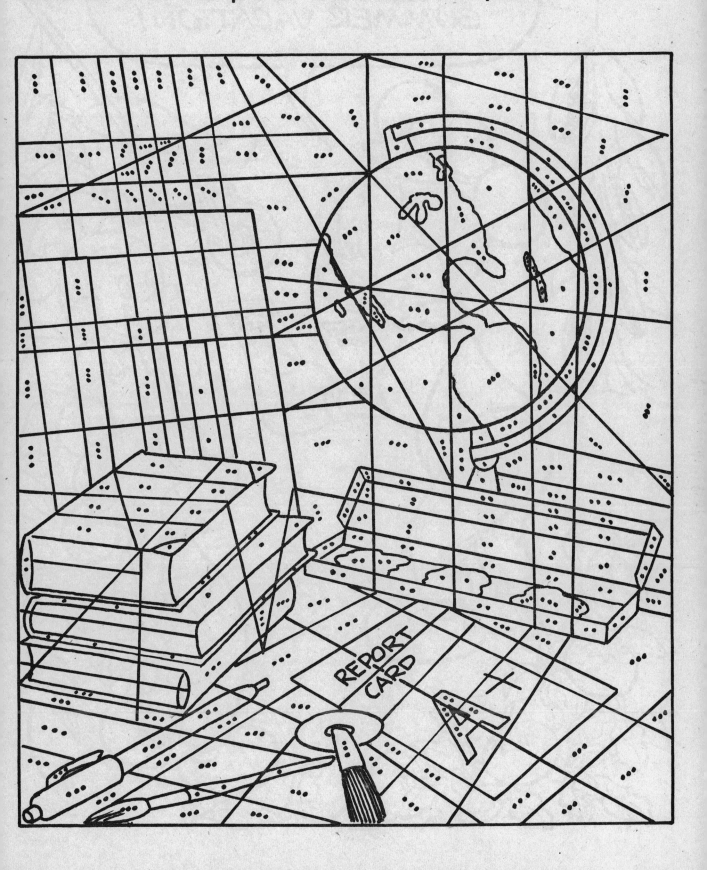

FIND ALL THE B WORDS.

Draw a circle around all of the things that begin with B.

A SECRET CODE

Morty knows what Mickey can do. Use the secret code to find out what Morty is thinking.

A	B	C	D	E	F	G	H	I	J
♡	✳	‖	＝	•	○	▢	◇	⦂	≡

K	L	M	N	O	P	Q	R	S	T
◤	↑	↔	▮	▽	/	∿	⧢	⦂	●

U	V	W	X	Y	Z
♥	∧	⦀	☆	↓	●

VACATION CROSSWORD PUZZLE

ACROSS:
4. A large body of water
7. To relax
8. Lodging for travellers
9. A canvas room to camp in

DOWN:
1. To get a tan, plan a trip in the _____.
2. To ski, go to a _____.
3. A sandy shore
5. To see Alaska, travel _____.
6. To go on a trip far away, take a _____.

DRAWING BOXES

Here is a game Morty and Ferdie are playing while they wait for Mickey. Each player takes one turn at a time connecting any two dots. The first player to complete a box puts his initials inside. The player who completes the most boxes wins.

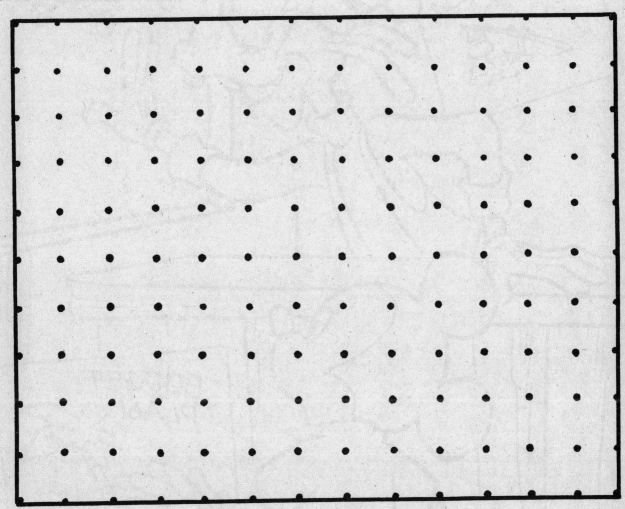

HELP
WANTED
—
TOUR
GUIDE

WHAT WILL MICKEY NEED?

Color in all the things a tour guide will need.

FESTIVAL

How many words can you make from the letters in festival? Write them in the blanks below.

VEST

_____

_____

_____

_____

_____

_____

_____

_____

LATE

_____

_____

_____

_____

_____

_____

_____

_____

HEFTY HANNAH

Begin with the F at the arrow and end with the starred S.
After finding the right path, copy the letters, in order, in
the blanks to find out how much Hefty Hannah weighs.

__ __ __ __   __ __ __ __ __ __ __

__ __ __ __ __ __

LOOK OUT BELOW

Try to avoid all the hazards and get Mickey to the bottom of the driveway safely.

THE TOUR
BEGINS

Read this story out loud. When you come to a blank, shut your eyes and point your finger somewhere on the opposite page. Then read the word that is under your fingertip.

"I just love vacations," said Minnie Mouse as she waited for the tour bus, holding her little _____ .

"Me too," said Morty, as he threw a _____ to Ferdie. "But I wish the _____ would hurry."

Soon the bus, carrying a _____ , four large _____s, and a _____ drove up. Minnie picked up her _____ and her new _____ with the striped _____ . "I'll need these on our trip," she said.

Morty sat down between Goofy, who was wearing _____s and Mickey who held a large _____ in his _____ . A _____ on top of it kept tickling Morty's _____ . He wiggled and his _____ fell out of his _____ and rolled away, making a sound like a _____ .

Suddenly Minnie screamed, "A _____ just flew in the _____ !"

Ferdie tried to swat it with a _____ . Goofy stopped the _____ . Mickey caught the _____ with his _____ and put it under a _____ on the side of the _____ . Then he picked a yellow _____ and gave it to Minnie.

"Thank you," Minnie said. "It goes with my little _____ .

At last they were at the _____ . Mickey and Goofy helped take ten _____s of _____s and a _____ of _____ off the bus. Everybody ran to the _____ .

"We'll have more _____ than a _____ of _____s," said Ferdie as he nibbled on salted _____s.

STEAMROLLER

TOASTER

MITTEN

FUZZBALL

MUDPIE

PUDDLE

FUR

NOSE

PIZZA

DOGFOOD

SKATEBOARD

BLOB

HIPPO

FIREPLUG

EYEBALL

DOORKNOB

PUDDLE

TOENAIL

PITCHFORK

SHOWER

VOLCANO

CLOWN

BATHTUB

LIVER

CIGAR

MUSTACHE

PIANO

DONKEY

Color the areas with one dot very lightly with any crayon. Use the same crayon to color the areas with two dots very dark. Color the areas without any dots white. The sign will look like neon.

WORD TRACKS

Begin at any letter and follow the track to other letters to make words. On Track 1, for example, you can make the words VACATION and TON. On Track 2, you can make the words MICKEY and TIME. See how many others you can make.

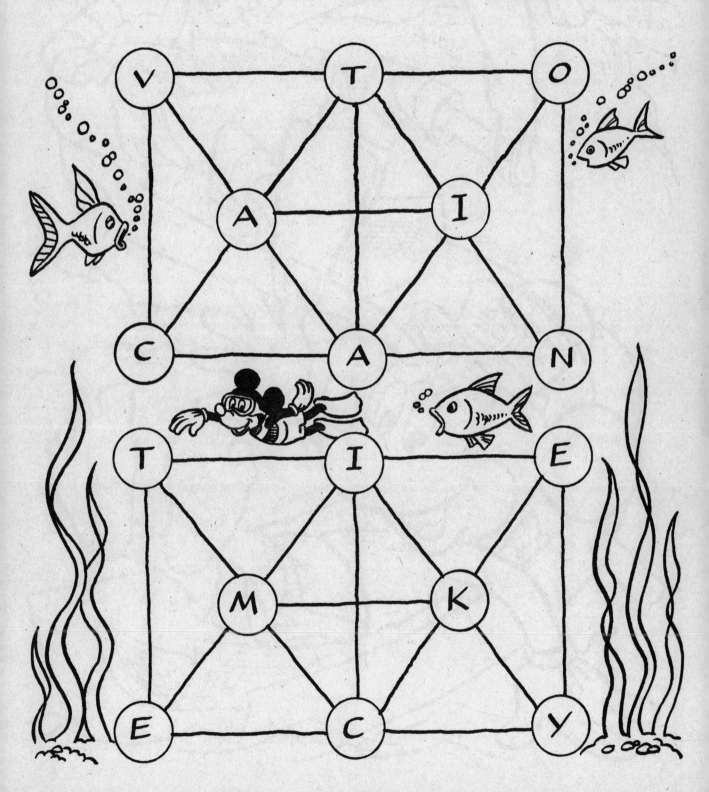

FIND MINNIE!

Only one of these is the real Minnie. Draw a circle around the Minnie that is different from all the others.

A SWIMMING TURTLE

Tear this page out and paste it on heavy paper with the turtle side up. Cut out the turtle along the dotted lines. Fill a large pan or bowl with water. Lay the turtle on the surface of the water. Pour a large drop of cooking oil in the hole in the turtle's back. The oil will spread out over the water and make the turtle move.

A FOSSIL DIG

Find all the dinosaurs hidden in the picture. Color them in.

WHAT DID PLUTO FIND?

Connect the dots, beginning at 1 to see what Pluto found.

Only one path will lead the group along the trail. Find the right starting point and follow the path by turning the way Mickey, Minnie, Pluto or Goofy tells you.

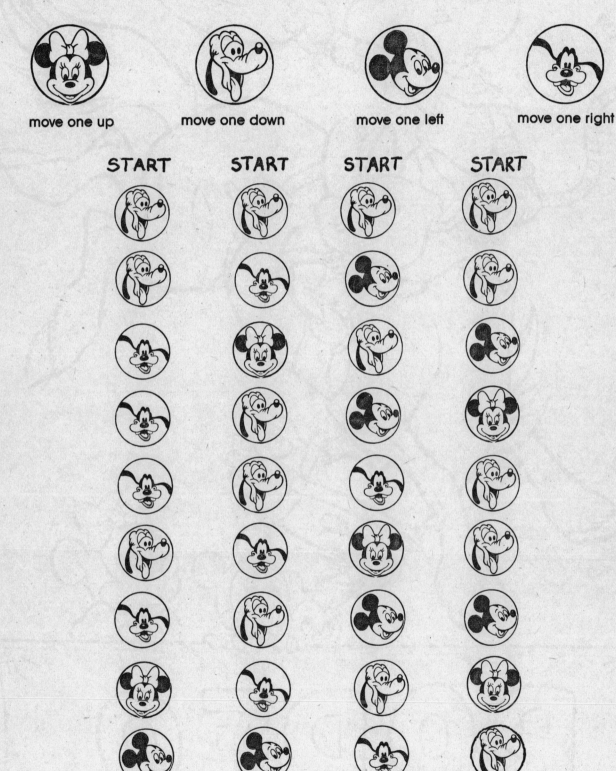

move one up   move one down   move one left   move one right

START   START   START   START

FINISH

RODEO

COWBOY MICKEY

Cut out the square with the picture of the bronco on it. Then cut along the dotted line near the top of the square. Now cut out the T shape with Mickey on it. Slide the T shape through the slot in the square. As you slide the T shape up and down, watch Mickey get bounced around.

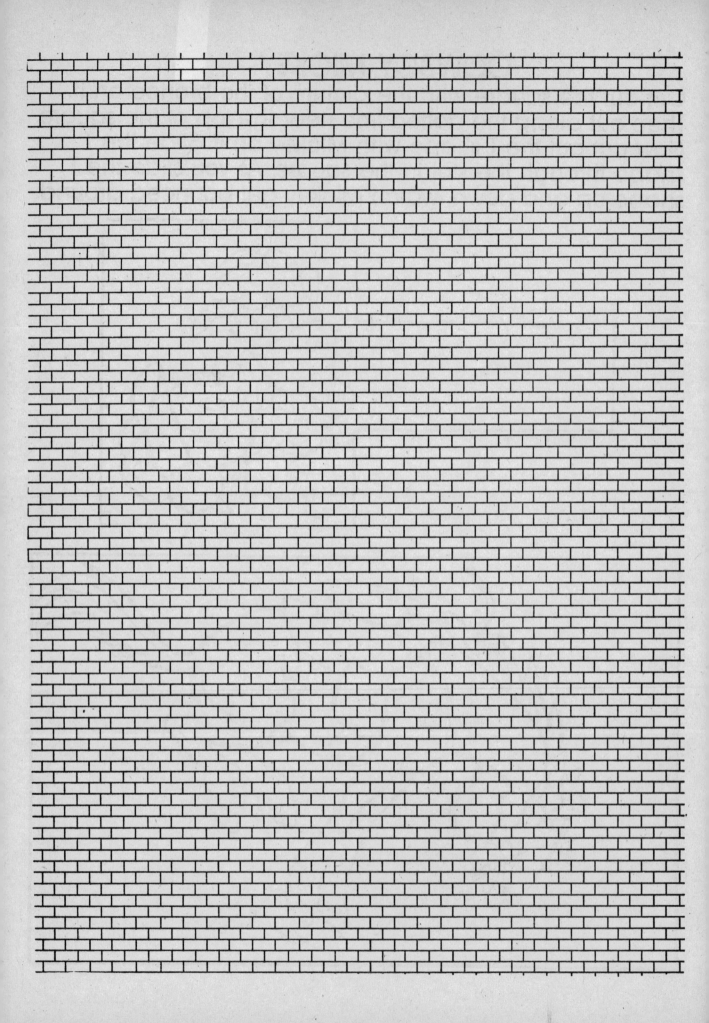

COWBOY CLOTHES

Mickey wants to get a real cowboy outfit. Can you help him unscramble the things on his list? The pictures of the cowboy clothes show what the scrambled words stand for.

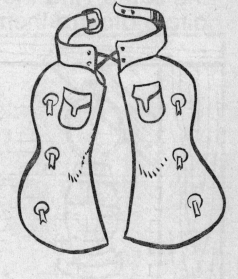

1. THA _____

2. OOBST _____

3. SSRUP _____

4. NBAAAND _____

5. SPHAC _____

Answers: hat, boots, spurs, bandana, chaps

MIRROR IMAGE

This picture is the mirror image of the one on the opposite page. But, if you look closely, not everything is the same. Find the things that are different and draw a circle around them.

Can you find all of the things in this picture that begin with R?

Morty has spotted danger ahead. Can you figure out what the danger is using the code below?

1. If a rabbit is softer than an alligator, write W in blank 1. If not, write X.
2. If a jet is slower than a train, write P in blank 2. If not, write A.
3. If a brick is heavier than a cottonball, write T in blank 3. If not, write L.
4. If a snowball is bigger than a raindrop, write E in blank 4. If not, write O.
5. If ten is more than a dozen, write S in blank 5. If not, write R.
6. If an orange is sweeter than a lemon, write F in blank 6. If not, write M.
7. If a centipede has more legs than an ant, write A in blank 7. If not, write U.
8. If Morty is bigger than Goofy, write R in blank 8. If not, write L.
9. If a car has more wheels than a bike, write L in blank 9. If not, write Y.

$$\overline{\quad}\ \overline{\quad}\ \overline{\quad}\ \overline{\quad}\ \overline{\quad}\ \overline{\quad}\ \overline{\quad}\ \overline{\quad}\ \overline{\quad}\ !$$
1. 2. 3. 4. 5. 6. 7. 8. 9.

A PATH TO SAFETY

Help Mickey find the only clear route across the river. Do not cross any lines.

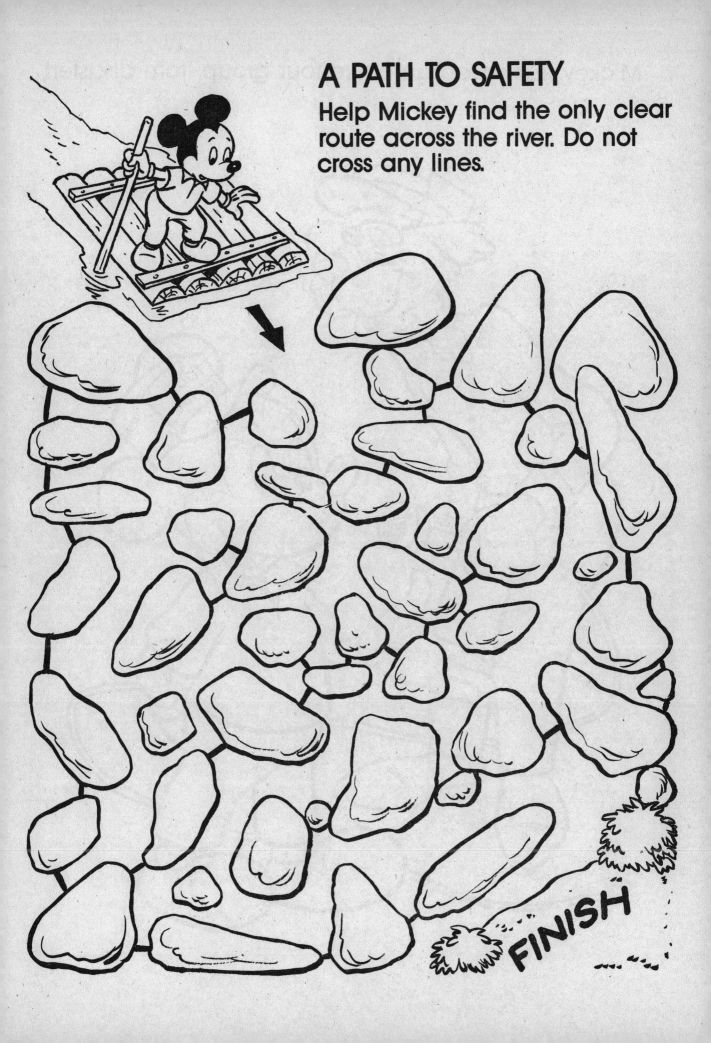

FINISH

Mickey has saved an entire tour group from disaster!

HOORAY FOR MICKEY MOUSE!

Unscramble the letters in each balloon to find out what color each one should be.

WHAT IS GOOFY DOING?

The tour is almost over, but poor Goofy has a problem.
Tear out this page and paste it on heavy paper.
Cut out the squares along the black lines. Put the pieces
together to make a picture. What is Goofy doing?

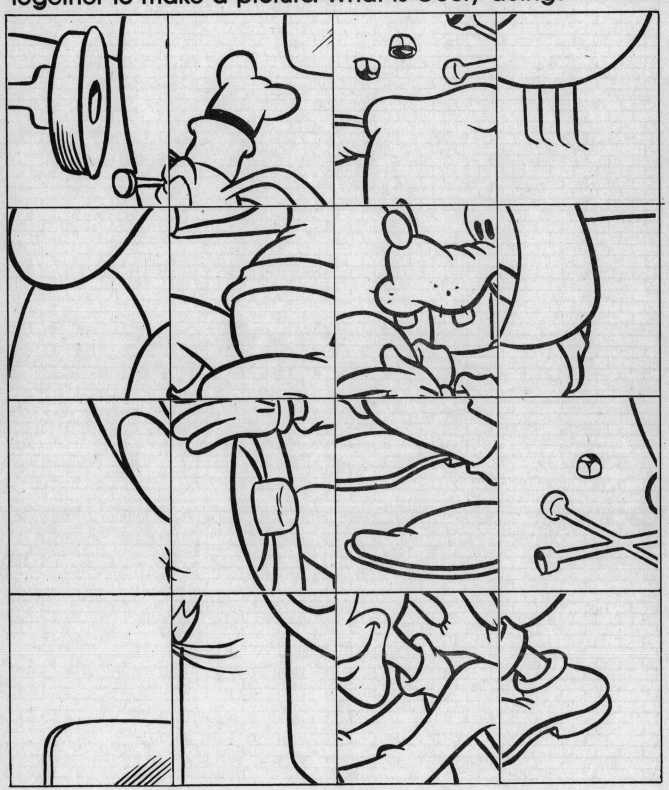

WHAT'S INSIDE?

Morty and Ferdie have a lot of things to unpack. Using the word list you see on the trunk, find the objects in the puzzle on the suitcase.

CAMERA
BINOCULARS
TOWEL
BOOK
SWEATER
SOCKS
TRUNKS
SHOES

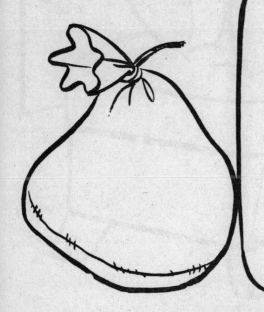

B I N O C U L A R S
T S W E A T T O C W
R L A R S W O S A E
U B O K R E W O M A
R X B O O K E C B T
T R U N K S L K O E
C A M E R A K S T R
N S H O E S S U X E